WILLIAM M. GAINES'S

THE DIRTY OLD MAD ®

ALBERT B. FELDSTEIN, Editor

WARNER BOOKS

A Warner Communications Company

With all the old movies being shown on television nowadays, our young people are suffering the same fate we older folks suffered: Mainly, they're being deluged by that corny old "Sure-Fire Dialogue." And so, this next article is MAD's idea of what it'd be like—

IF

KIDS USED MOVIE CLICHÉS

IN EVERYDAY LIFE

ARTIST: PAUL COKER, JR.
WRITER: HARRY PURVIS

THERE'S A SOCCER BORN EVERY MINUTE DEPT.

For years, the nation's educators have been howling about the evils inherent in such big time college sports as football and basketball. They contend that there's too much professionalism, that not enough boys have a chance to participate, etc. But no one really lifted a finger to correct the situation until MAD's Athletic Council went to work—and he's come up with a brand new sport that promises to provide good, clean amateur fun for all. Here, then, are the rules for this great new national pastime of the future. Digest them carefully and be the last person in your neighborhood to play . . . as . . .

MAD MAGAZINE introduces 43-MAN SQUAMISH

ARTIST: GEORGE WOODBRIDGE

WRITER: TOM KOCH

A Squamish team consists of 43 players: the left & right
Inside Grouches, the left & right Outside Grouches, four
Deep Brooders, four Shallow Brooders, five Wicket Men,

Each player is equipped with a long hooked stick known as
a Frullip. The Frullip is used to halt opposing players
attempting to cross your goal line with the Pritz (ball).
The Official Pritz is 3¾ inches in diameter and is made
of untreated Ibex hide stuffed with Blue Jay feathers.

three Offensive Niblings, four Quarter-Frummerts, two Half-Frummerts, one Full-Frummert, two Overblats, two Underblats, nine Back-Up Finks, two Leapers and a Dummy.

Play begins with the Probate Judge flipping a new Spanish peseta. If the Visiting Captain calls the toss correctly, the game is immediately cancelled. If he fails to call it correctly, then the Home Team Captain is given his choice of either carrying the Pritz . . . or defending against it.

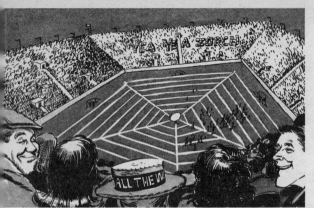

The game of Squamish is played on a 5-sided field known as a Flutney. The two teams line up at opposite sides of the Flutney and play seven Ogres of fifteen minutes each —unless it rains, in which case they play eight Ogres.

The defending right Outside Grouch signifies that he is ready to hurl the Pritz by shouting, "Mi Tio es infermo, pero la carretera es verde!"—a wise old Chilean proverb that means, "My Uncle is sick, but the highway is green!"

The offensive team, upon receiving the Pritz, has five Snivels in which to advance to the enemy goal. If they do it on the ground, it's a Woomik and counts 17 points. If they hit it across with their Frullips, it's a Durmish which only counts 11 points. Only the offensive Niblings and Overblats are allowed to score in the first 6 Ogres.

Special rules, applicable only during the seventh Ogre, turn the game into something very akin to Buck Euchre. During this final Ogre (and the eighth, if it rains), the four Quarter-Frummerts are permitted to either kick or throw the Pritz, and the nine Finks are allowed to heckle the opposition by doing imitations of Barry Goldwater.

A typical seventh Ogre play is shown below. Team "A"—trailing 516—209, is in possession of the Pritz with fourth Snivel and half the Flutney to go. Suddenly, the left Underblat, going for the big one, sends two Shallow Brooders and the Full-Frummert downfield. Obviously, he is going to try for a Woomik when the opposition expects a Durmish. A daring play of this type invariably brings the crowd rising to its feet and heading for the exits.

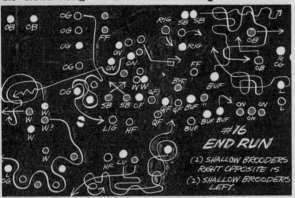

#16
END RUN

(2) SHALLOW BROODERS
RIGHT OPPOSITE IS
(2) SHALLOW BROODERS
LEFT.

A variety of penalties keep play from getting out of hand. Walling the Pritz, Frullip-gouging, icing on fifth Snivel, running with the mob and raunching are all minor infractions subject to a ten-yard penalty. Major infractions (sending the Dummy home early, interfering with Wicket Men, rushing the season, bowing to the inevitable and inability to face facts) are punishable by loss of half the Flutney, except when the Yellow Caution Flag is out.

Squamish rules provide for 4 officials: a Probate Judge, a Field Representative, a Head Cockswain and a Baggage Smasher. None has any authority after play has begun. In the event of a disagreement between the officials, a final decision is left up to the spectator who left his car in the parking lot with the lights on and the motor running.

In the event of a tie score, the teams play a sudden-death overtime. The exception to this rule occurs when opposing Left Overblats are both out of the game on personal fouls. When such is the case, the two teams line up on opposite sides of the Flutney and settle the tie by shouting dirty limericks at each other until one team breaks up laughing.

Amateur Squamish players are strictly forbidden to accept subsidies, endorse products, make collect phone calls or eat garlic. Otherwise, they lose their amateur standing. A player may turn Pro, however, merely by throwing a game.

The original charter calls for an annual meeting of the National Squamish Rules Committee. At its inaugural meeting, the committee approved a re-wording of Article XVI, Paragraph 77, Section J of the rules. This section, which formerly read: "The offensive left Underblat, in all even-numbered Ogres, must touch down his Frullip at the edge of the Flutney and signal to the Head Cockswain that he is ready for play to continue," has now been simplified

Schools with small enrollments which preclude participation in 43-Man Squamish may play a simplified version of the game: 2-Man Squamish. The rules are identical, except that in 2-Man Squamish, the object of the game is to lose.

to read: "The offensive left Underblat, in all even-numbered ogres, must touch down his Frullip at the edge of the Flutney and signal to either the Head Cockswain, or to any other official to whom the Head Cockswain may have delegated this authority in writing and in the presence of two witnesses, both of whom shall have been approved and found to be of high moral character by the Office of the Commissioner, that he is ready for play to continue."

THE MODERN HIGHWAYMAN

With apologies to Alfred Noyes

Illustrated by Don Martin

Written by James T. Shannon

The wind was a torrent of darkness, running an endless race.
The moon was a silvery rocket, careening through outer space.
The road was bathed in neon, a pagan for man to anoint,
And the highwayman came driving -
    Driving — driving —
The highwayman came driving, to "Charlie's Hamburger Joint."

He'd a baseball cap on his forehead, a short goatee at his chin.
A jacket of smooth, black leather, and dungarees neat as a pin
(Except for a few random grease spots): his engineer boots reached his thigh.
And he rode with a jewelled twinkle,
    His stick-on-the-floor a-twinkle,
His stolen hubcaps a-twinkle, under the jewelled sky.

He kicked up dust in the driveway and screeched to a halt in the lot.
He raced his engine a few times, to call to the heart of his heart.
He leaned on his horn for a minute, and who should come from the back
But Charlie's black-eyed daughter,
    Shirley, the owner's daughter,
Aglow with her blue eye-shadow, and munching on a snack.

Amid dark in the dark, old kitchen, a French-fry basket fell,
Where Clyde, the dishwasher, listened, listened as one in a spell.
His eyes were orbs of anger, his hair was uncut hay,
But he loved old Charlie's daughter,
    His boss' swinging daughter,
Mute as a moose he listened and heard the dragster say:

"How 'bout a kiss, huh, Shirley? I'm draggin' this fink t'night,
An' I'll be back with his double-fin, unless he puts up a fight.
But if he won't han' it over, an' I use my wrench on his head,
    Then look for me t'morra night,
        Watch for me t'morra night,
I'll come an' see ya t'morra night," the bold daredevil said.

He shifted into neutral and rose from his bucket-seat,
And would have kissed his Shirley, but she continued to eat.
She stopped her munching long enough to blow a kiss his way.
And she waved her hand in the moonlight,
    (Fair, fragile hand in the moonlight),
Then he shifted to first in the moonlight and wheeled off to the fray.

There were no wheels screeching at breakfast as Shirley downed her eggs.
And no horn blaring at lunchtime and her dozen chicken legs.
She had finished a couple of pizzas and she was saying her pre-supper grace,
    Screaming — screaming —
Old John Fuzz came screaming into her daddy's place.

They said not a word to Charlie. They drank their coffee black.
But they warned his daughter, Shirley, to stay out of the back,
For they knew she loved the highwayman and longed to be his bride,
And they sat on two stools by the window;
    And they watched the road through the window,
And she moaned as she looked through the window, at the road that he would ride.

The road, with its neon luster, stretched out like a sleeping snake.
She nervously nibbled her lower lip and reached for some chocolate cake.
When, Lo and Behold! by the cake tin, old Charlie's truck keys lay.
A circle of gold on the counter,
    She reached for them there on the counter;
Her fingers were two inches from them, when her father walked over to say:

"If you try to help your boyfriend while those two cossacks are here,
They could make me close this place up and go to jail for a year.
So if you try to warn him in any manner or way,
Then you go right on a diet,
     A bare, subsistence diet;
Not one snack more will I let you eat till they cart my corpse away!"

Her fingers retreated like pipers across a formica beach.
The circlet of keys tantalized her, just within her reach.
Yet the mountain of sweet chocolate dared her, Satan in Pillsbury form,
And visions of food warmed her senses,
     Eclairs and pies burned her senses;
Pizzas and malts seared her senses and began an emotional storm.

The cops in their seats by the window spoke in Neanderthal tones.
The fever to catch the highwayman coursed a white-hot stream through their bones.
They muttered of burning his license, their voices grew louder, and then—
Shirley's dream world vanished!

    All dreams of food were banished;
She turned her back on the chocolate cake, never to taste it again.

Her fingers slid over the counter, the cold keys kissed her hand.
With forced-ease she walked from the counter and stood by the newspaper stand.
And there at the stand near the doorway, she guarded the road with her ear,
Till she thought she heard the growling,

    The old, familiar growling;
Then she looked down the stretch of the highway and saw her love drawing near!

She glanced at the cops. Had they heard it? It seemed like an earthquake to her!
But their noses were still in their coffee, their beady, black eyes didn't stir.
The engine grew louder and louder! Her lover came nearer, so near!
Then a gust of night air filled the diner,
    As Shirley slipped out of the diner;
She flew like a shot from the diner, her heart slowly sinking with fear.

Up, up to the truck's seat she vaulted. She jiggled the key in the slot.
Then, coughing, the engine turned over. On two wheels she tore from the lot!
She slammed the truck into second, down the road to her lover she sped.
And she blasted the truck horn to warn him;
    Off and on went the headlights to warn him;
She did all she could think of to warn him of the trap that was waiting ahead.

Her hopes leapt like flames as she saw him pull off to the side of the road.
She'd saved him! He'd turn and escape them. Her heart was relieved of its load.
She heard a dull wail from the diner; a siren that only warned "cop."
Then the highwayman turned in the highway,
    He turned his car 'round in the highway;
In a flash he had turned in the highway. But then, Shirley saw her love stop!

And still on a summer's night, they say, when the wind starts its endless race,
When the moon is a silvery rocket, careening through outer space,
When the road is bathed in neon, a pagan for man to anoint,

"The fool!" thought Shirley, "He's crazy!" (There was surely no time for delay!)
Before her, the highwayman waited; behind came the wolves for the prey.
Too late! The squad car flashed by her. Oh, why did the highwayman lag?
He had heard her horn blaring to warn him,
    And seen the lights flashing to warn him;
But he didn't hear cops coming for him, he was so damn anxious to drag!

A highwayman comes riding—
    Riding—riding—
A highwayman comes riding, to "Charlie's Hamburger Joint."

He spins his tires in the driveway and brakes to a halt in the lot.
He leans his bicycle near the door and calls for the heart of his heart.
He jingles his bell a few times; a specter from out the back sails.
It's Charlie's black-eyed daughter!
  Shirley, the owner's daughter!
Aglow with her blue eye-shadow and chewing on her nails.

JOKE AND DAGGER DEPT. PART II

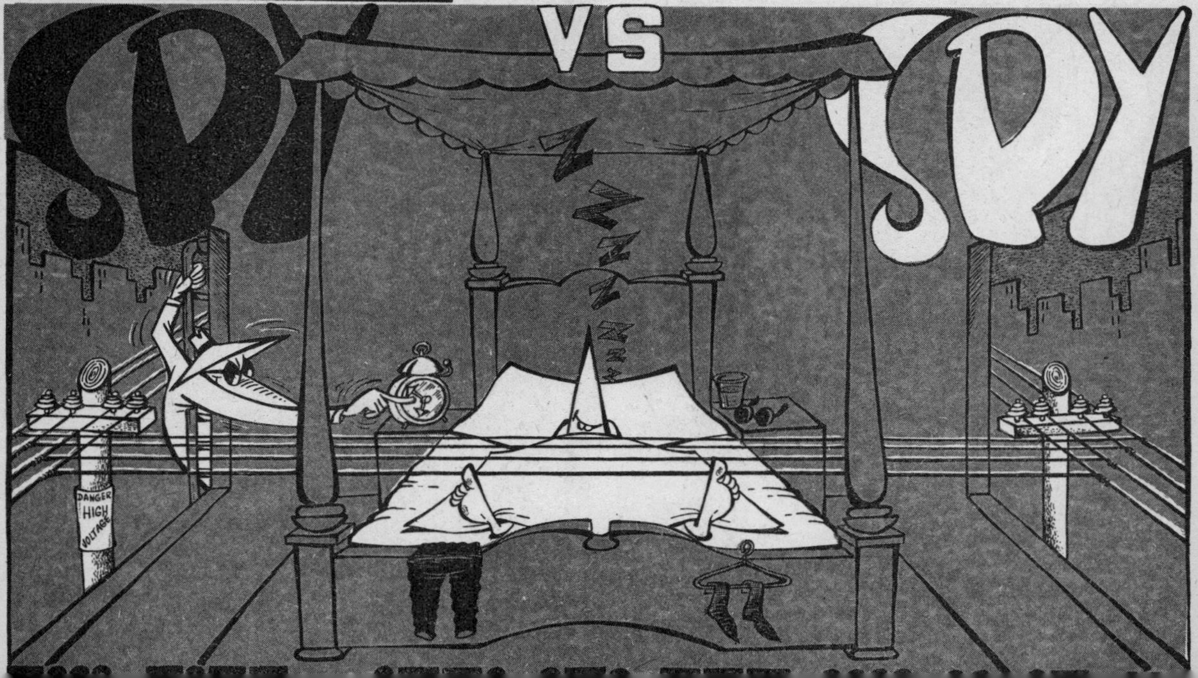

NUTS WITH BOLTS DEPT.

As you may or may not know, MAD currently has a circulation of approximately 1,650,000 copies per issue and, what with pass-on readership, we figure that we've probably got about 7,000,000 readers. Now, then... how many of you 7,000,000 readers would like to see us publish another Primer? Good! Here is a Primer for *both* of you — entitled ...

THE MAD
GUN
OWNERS
AND OTHER
SMALL BORES
PRIMER

Written by Larry Siegel
Illustrated by George Woodbridge

LESSON ONE

See the nice man.
The nice man is a Gun Owner.
Gun Owners are very fond of their guns.
They kiss them a lot.
See the nice man kiss his Luger.
Kiss, kiss, kiss.
Is he in love with his Luger?
Of course not, silly!
How could this man get serious with a German gun?
It would never work out.
They are of different nationalities.
Let's just say that they are good friends.

LESSON TWO

See the nice man now.
He is hunting with another of his guns.
See him shoot the pretty deer.
Bang, bang, bang.
See the pretty deer's blood gush.
Gush, gush, gush.
What fun they are having!
See how happy the hunter is.
See how happy the hunter's dog is.
The pretty deer is not happy.
He is a spoil-sport.

LESSON THREE

Oh, isn't this funny?
The pretty deer is not dead yet.
He is only wounded.
See the man pump more bullets into him.
Pump, bang, pump, bang.
Hunting is such a wonderful sport.
It is a lot more fun than other sports
Like Baseball,
And Football,
And Spanish Inquisitions.

LESSON FOUR

Look, the nice man is walking away.
He is leaving the deer to rot.
Aren't you going to eat the deer, nice man?
After all, you killed him.
And deer meat is very tasty.
Isn't this funny?
Do you know why the man won't eat the deer?
Because he is a vegetarian!
Ha, ha, ha.
Perhaps instead of shooting a deer next time,
Why doesn't the nice man shoot a head of lettuce?

LESSON FIVE

Here is another Gun Lover.
He keeps a pistol in his desk drawer.
It gives him a sense of power.
So he keeps his gun handy.
He keeps his gun very handy.
His children have no trouble finding it.
His family has been shrinking every day.
Shrink, shrink, shrink.
Aren't guns great for beating the Population Explosion?

LESSON SIX

See the other man.
He is running for Congress.
He wants to do away with all taxes.
He wants to abolish the Supreme Court.
He wants private ownership of the CIA.
He is some kind of nut.
But he will be elected.
Do you know why he will be elected?
Because all the Gun Owners will vote for him.
Why will they vote for him?
Because he is also against any new law
Which will require registration of firearms.
He claims that if there is a war,
We might be invaded by Communists,
And we will all need guns.
With nuts like that in Congress,
It could happen.

LESSON SEVEN

See the gun store.
Anybody can buy a gun and ammunition here.
See the people shopping for guns.
Shop, shop, shop.
See the nice lady.
She is bargain-hunting.
She wants to do away with her husband.
Because he's no bargain.
See her buy a pistol for $8.00,
And a bullet for 9¢.
Wait, nice lady! Don't go yet! Think . . .
You forgot your green stamps!

LESSON EIGHT

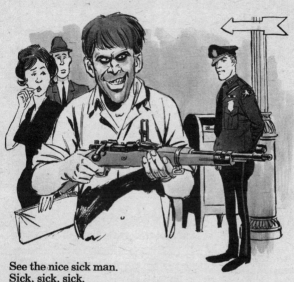

See the nice sick man.
Sick, sick, sick.
He bought his gun through the mail.
What is he going to do now?
He is going to shoot someone he doesn't like.
Why don't the police arrest him?
Because he is not carrying a concealed weapon.
He is carrying it in the open for all to see.
Later on the police will arrest him.
After he shoots the person he doesn't like.
Aren't you glad that justice is blind?

GUNS GUNS GUNS!

AUTHENTIC DELUXE ELEPHANT GUN

ONLY $7⁹⁵*

Here it is, sports lovers . . . the authentic deluxe elephant gun you've been waiting for! Fires .944 calibre shells and/or small Civil War-type cannonballs. Deadly accurate from 200-500 yards. After that, who knows what you'll hit! Wonderful for flattening big game or overweight people you don't happen to like very much.

✱ NO MONEY DOWN. TAKE 18 YEARS (OR LONGER) TO PAY.

CREDIT REFERENCES DISCOURAGED

FINK'S SPORTING GOODS
226 West Slaughter Street, Bangor, Maine

> **NOTE:** We are required by law to have all mail-order purchasers send us a signed statement to the effect that you are 21 years of age or over, not an alien, have never been convicted of a crime, are not now under indictment, are not a fugitive, and are not a drug addict. Naturally, we have no way of checking the authenticity of your statement. So we'll sell merchandise to anybody. Just remember what happens when you lie. You could get a pimple on your tongue!

LESSON NINE

See the typical magazine ad.
See how easy it is to buy guns by mail.
Isn't it fun to buy lethal weapons by mail?
Where is your friendly Postmaster?

He is busy searching for obscene mail.
Search, search, search.
He wants to make sure that sick people
Who order lethal weapons by mail
Have clean minds.

ONE FOR THE ROAD DEPT.

It takes thousands of nuts to put a car together, but it only takes one nut to scatter a car all over the road. This article is dedicated to the thousands of nuts who put cars together—and *then* scatter them all over the road. Mainly, here is our version of the type of magazines they read

CUSTOMIZE YOUR '65 MUSTANG INTO A '39 DODGE FOR LESS THAN $16,000

LOAD & CRASH

THE HIGH INSURANCE RISK'S MAGAZINE

NOVEMBER 1965   3/6 IN ENGLAND   60¢ IN CANADA $145 INCLUDING FUNERAL AT FORESTLAWN

Tooling Through Mexico in the new Finsta Potra Z-B

9.716 M.P.H. AT SEBRING ON A SOUPED-UP MASSEY-FERGUSON TRACTOR

SHORT-SHORT FEATURE: THE KAISER-FRAZER ERA IN AMERICAN MOTORING

I Flunked My Driver's Test In a 340 HP Ferrari

EXTREMELY SHORT-SHORT FEATURE: THE EDSEL ERA IN AMERICAN MOTORING

THINGS TO COME: A SNEAK PREVIEW OF THE 1966 CADILLAC MAIL TRUCK

Is The '29 Essex A True Classic? * Getting Car Sick In An Alfa-Romeo

ARTIST: GEORGE WOODBRIDGE   WRITER: TOM KOCH

WHAT'S NEW

THE LATEST FROM MOTORDOM'S MARKETPLACE

The Classic Marmon V-16 in kit form is the latest offering of Monstrous Motor Models, Racine, Wis. No auto enthusiast will want to pass up the chance to create his own replica of this famous vintage machine. Scaled down to parts too small to be grasped by human fingers, it's the ideal gift for driving Dad or other annoying relatives out of their minds.   Price $4.98

The Copy Cat Manufacturing Co. of Sarasota, Fla., has begun production of authentic full size replicas of the fabulous Model T. An ideal attention-getter for all business and promotional purposes, the modern version is an exact copy of its famed great-granddaddy, even down to such details as the unperfected transmission which caused the original to slip into high gear while unoccupied. Henry Ford sold 15,000,000 of these durable cars for $290. Now a sparkling new replica can be yours for $2,250 F.O.B. Sarasota, Florida.

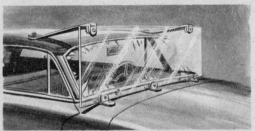

Dangerous distortion created by modern curved windshields is ended forever with this flat, perpendicular replacement recently put on the market by the Eagle-Eye Glass Co. of Latrobe, Pa. A leading producer of auto windshields, until the invention of safety glass forced the firm to the brink of bankruptcy, Eagle-Eye now bounces back stronger than ever to correct the bungles of larger manufacturers. Guaranteed to provide normal road vision through the clever use of uncurved, untinted plate glass, Eagle-Eye windshields can be easily installed by the do-it-yourselfer once the hazardous original equipment on late model cars had been smashed and disposed of.   Price $35.98

TECHNICAL TALKS

by Edith Barnstable

I have done a thorough job of souping up my '24 Stearns-Knight with dual carbs, a full-blown house, Smitty muffler, etc. However at the same time I was overhauling the engine, I installed square wheels. I figured that the finished product would do at least 110 M.P.H. But for some reason, it won't move at all. What do you think my trouble might be?

—M.M.C., Salt Lake City

The '24 Stearns-Knight was a straight six with overhead cams. It was never meant to be equipped with dual carbs. The trouble may be there, or it may that the car is moving but that all the scenery around Salt Lake City looks so much alike that you have the illusion of standing still.

I have had a tappet noise in my head for almost 10,000,000 miles now. The head of my car, I mean. It is a '51 Blewitt, a make which never got into full production for a number of reasons, mostly legal. I have rebored the head, stymied the vale sleeves, grannished the crankcase, unduffered the pistons and shuffled the rods. However, I still have the tappet noise. Is this possible?

—W.S.P., Loon Lake, Ore.

Yes.

The instruction manual that came with my '54 Chevy says that the windshield should be washed occasionally. What does this mean?

—L.C.F., Akron, Ohio

Auto instruction manuals often use terms which apply to one make or year, but not to others. A qualified mechanic may be able to help you with this problem, but I doubt it.

Is it true that '65 Paisano-Lasagna has gauges registering ergs per RPM, AC-DC voltage, foot-pounds per man-hours, and minutes left to play?

—C.C.D., Kansas City, Kan.

Only the J-660 and X-K-L models, neither of which are available in this country.

I have been itching to get behind the wheel of the new 400 HP Maserati Runabout to see what those 400 horses can really do. Can you give me any advice before I buy it?

—D.A.F., St. Louis, Mo.

You will find that scratching without bumping into the Overdrive Switch on the 400 HP Maserati Runabout is a factor that any potential buyer with a skin irritation should give more than passing consideration.

DRIVEL
FROM
DETROIT

Forecasts And Facts From The Motor Capital

A TOURING CAR BY KAISER-WILLYS FOR '66?

A survey by the firm's History Department, designed to discover which of the company's failures had been longest endured by the public before going blooey, arouses industry speculation that the 1920 Overland may be put back into production for the 1966 model year. With such notable fiascoes as the *Frazer*, the *American* and the sporty *Jeepster* ranking high on the list of all-time automotive blunders, the sturdy *Overland* shapes up as the company's best hope for the future. Executives remain mum, and the inside word is that leaders of the firm are split over the issue of isinglass curtains for the new entry in the medium priced field.

BUGS REMAIN IN PIERCE-ARROW'S JET.

Word from the supposedly-abandoned *Pierce-Arrow* proving ground has it that the company's bid for a comeback with a jet-propelled sportster may be delayed until 1973 or 1974. Whispers emanating from the rumor mill indicate that a few bugs have yet to be worked out of the engine, and that the first jet test-car incinerated four mechanics standing behind it and caused the whole east wing of the factory to be destroyed by flames.

DO TIRE MANUFACTURERS KNOW MORE THAN THEY'RE LETTING ON?

According to the most reliable reports filtering into the motor capital from Akron, probably not.

VOLKSWAGEN MAY MOVE TO DETROIT.

At least, so goes the story making the rounds in the motor capital. Probable reason: VW plans to scrap its beetle design after almost 20 years in favor of an updated version replete with massive chrome, high tail fins and power extras, all set on a frame approximately four feet longer than that of the current model. With American motorists shaping up as the only potential buyers in the world, VW brass may well close down the German plant completely and move all operations to the U.S.A.

A CHEVIAC BY G.M. FOR 1967?

General Motors officials reportedly have found a small hole in their present price line which may be filled in '67 with the introduction of a new car to plug the gap between the Chevrolet Impala (top price $2,980.50) and the standard Pontiac (base price $2,983.75) With Corvair, Chevelle and Chevy II already overlapping nicely to the complete bewilderment of the public, the new line, tentatively labelled the Cheviac, appears a natural for the shopping motorist with $2,982.12½ to spend.

SWAP 'N' SWINDLE

FOR SALE

'27 WILLS ST. CLAIRE 3-dr. ambulance. Only one of its kind ever built due to failure of small engine to propel oversized body. Parts impossible to buy, but makes wonderful sleep-out shelter for the kiddies. Terrible condition, but easily restored by any one crazy enough to want it. $800. L. L. Schlepp, 484 Rolling Meadow Lane, Brooklyn, N. Y.

'65 ROCCO-BAMBINI Super Sport Fastback. Never driven by present owner. In fact, physical proportions of previous owner are inconceivable. Speedometer reads 500 miles, all clocked under

careful supervision at Indianapolis Speedway. Original cost $22,000. Sacrifice for $21,995. Leadfoot Lindstrom, Box 7, Bonneville, Utah.

1837 FRONTIER LANDAU CONVERTIBLE. Believed to be the oldest classic auto in existence. Complete, except for the two horses apparently used by the original owner to pull it. Ideal for display use or helping other classic car owners form a circle in case of an Indian attack. $1,975. Rufe Strettlemayer c/o Bunt Farm, P.O. 47, Upper Gulch, Wyo.

WANTED

LEFT HEADLIGHT for '31 Hudson. No owners of right headlight need apply. Please do not send me any more right ones as this type can only be fitted into left bracket by reverse placement causing beam to shine toward rear of car. I am sick and tired of receiving right headlights, many arriving with postage due. I already have a right headlight, and as a taxpaying American, resent this indifference of the general public toward my previous ads. Disgusted, Box 779, West Covina, Calif.

BATTERY CHARGER suitable for use with either Model 550 Detroit Electric Phaeton, or Model 3-D Eveready Flashlight. Newby, 217 Warren Hull Memorial Drive, Beverly Hills, Cal.

WILL SWAP

CLASSIC '41 CHEVY—4 Dr. Sedan. Faded maroon, loose connecting rods, shot transmission and many other extras. Will trade this dandy collectors item for any common '63 or '64 convertible. Lucas Fribble, State Unemployment Office, Waiting Line 6, Chicago, Ill.

LIFETIME MEMBERSHIP IN DANCE STUDIO. Original cost $17,000. Will trade for any kind of car. I gotta get away from these crooks. I. M. Schlemiel, Cha-Cha Drive, Ft. Wayne, Ind.

RARE BACK NUMBERS OF EARLY AUTO MAGAZINES, recently found in my waiting room under later issues of Colliers. Will swap for X-Ray Outfit or impressively-framed Medical School Diploma. Dr. Nimble Kwaque, Suite 557, Peddlers of Mercy Building, Dayton, Ohio.

Test Driving The All-New Shakibutsu
Micro-Mini-Midget V-Zero

By Len Furdy

IT WOULD APPEAR that Shakibutsu's incredible engineering team of Wun-Cheep Nip and O. So-Slik has done it again. Placing an easily-broken coil spring power plant inside a flimsy rolled-tin body, the pair has come up with an economical run-about that combines the easy maneuverability of a compact with the type of unbelievable workmanship that American motorists have come to expect from Shakibutsu.

The author went through the unique experience of piloting the Far Eastern firm's entry in the 1964 Mobilgas Economy Run. Finishing the cross-country jaunt less than a year later, I felt that I had given the Micro-Mini-Midget a fair trial under all types of driving conditions, and found it a car that defies description in virtually every category. The Mobilgas people apparently shared my opinion after discovering that the wind-up motor has propelled the trim little V-Zero 3,261 miles on no gasoline at all. The result of the record smashing performance was federal legislation jammed through Congress by the oil lobby which places a $1,700 import tax on every Micro-Mini-Midget carried into this country.

The new tax added to the factory's suggested P.O.E. retail price of $7.98 places Shakibutsu's stripped down model in the ridiculous position of competing with the Volkswagen and a handful of domestic compacts. Officials of the Tokyo based firm frankly admit that their sole hope of gaining a foothold in the U.S. market is to push the V-Zero as a third car for American families with two-car garages.

In design, the V-Zero has undergone only a minor face-lifting since the Christmas season of 1963 when a pedal-driven version was introduced as a gift item for the 3-to-8-year-old group. The interior remains starkly simple. The author found the instrument panel easy to read, but this

convenience is somewhat diminished by the fact that the gauges are merely printed on cardboard, glued to the metal dash, and otherwise not connected to anything.

Trunk space is described by the manufacturer in cubic millimeters, creating the illusion that something larger than a box of cough drops can be carried in it. However, careful

(cont. on page 97)

Road Test Results

GENERAL

Curb weight ....6 lbs. 11 oz.
Wheelbase ....19½ in.
Over-all length ....23 in.
Height ....14½ in.
Steering type ....Piano wire &
                        chewing gum.
Turning radius ....2¾ ft.

SPECIFICATIONS

Engine type ......wind-up, utilizing
                  standard skate key.
Arrangement ....36 mos. to pay.
Horsepower ....7/100 @ 6 rpm.
Mantle ....310.
Torque @ rpm lb-ft ....
                     Howzzat again?
Bore ....utter

PRICE

Basic list at P.O.E. $7.98
Delivered price including taxes,
  accessories, etc. $2,007.98

PERFORMANCE

Top speed ....4½ mph.
Acceleration:
  0-1 mph..58 sec.
  0-2 mph..3 min., 44 sec.
  0-3 mph..49 min., 12 sec.
  0-4 mph..3 hrs., 6 min., 23 sec.
  0-top speed ....About 2 days.

SPEEDOMETER ERROR

40 mph indicated, Actual 1.7 mph.
90 mph indicated, Actual 3.1 mph.

THREE YEARS WORK RESTORING AN APPERSON JACK RABBIT

by Waldo Boomschlager

BEFORE

I GUESS I'LL NEVER FORGET Aug. 23, 1955. That was the date I stumbled across my big find, a 1916 Apperson Jack Rabbit in restorable condition sitting quietly in a barn lot near Neenah, Wis.

Evelyn, whom I had planned at the time to marry but later didn't, was with me as we made our way unsuspectingly down the back country road. We were really in search of milk glass, which Evelyn collects and which still abounds in that part of the country.

Evelyn already had 700 pieces of the beautiful glass, most of which she had inherited from her late aunt who had resided in Elkhart, Ind. The aunt, whose name, as I recall, was either Birdie Wingate or Esther Agnew, had never married, but rather had devoted her life to the milk glass collection.

Miss Wingate (or Miss Agnew) had been engaged at one time to a Cpl. Wilfred Hungerford who lived just outside of Elkhart on one of the major inter-urban lines. But Cpl. Hungerford became a mail handler on the old South Bend, Toledo and Spokane Railroad and ultimately married a girl half his age.

In time, the South Bend, Toledo and Spokane merged with the Pere Marquette to become the Southern Pacific in one of the more bold strokes of finance put over by Jay Hannah.

Hannah's original plan had merely been to extend the lines of the Baltimore and Ohio to Honolulu. But before the track laying had progressed more than 200 miles west of San Francisco, the entire venture was abandoned as impractical.

Hannah's decision to give up the Honolulu branch was thought to be directly responsible for the suicide of Romney L. Gruber, who had been selected to head that division. Gruber mentioned only poor health in the note he left, and it is true that he had been suffering from hemorrhoids since shortly after the Spanish-American war. But those who knew

(cont. on page 97)

AFTER

SPONSOR SPEAK WITH FORKED TONGUE DEPT.

Do you listen closely to TV commercials? Of course not! That's what the sponsors and their flunkies at the advertising agencies count on when they plan their messages—that you won't really be paying attention. Because they fill their sales pitches with cleverly worded phrases and facts that sound like one thing, but actually mean another. Watch now, as MAD exposes . . .

UNSPOKEN MESSAGES IN TV COMMERCIALS

ARTIST: JOE ORLANDO   WRITER: TOM KOCH

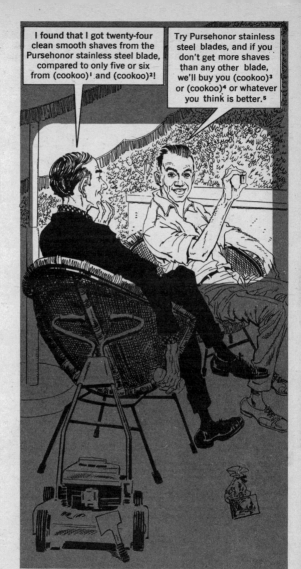

1—My Briggs & Stratton power lawn mower.
2—My oldest son's Boy Scout axe.
3—A picture post-card of Yellowstone Park.
4—A small bag of licorice jelly beans.
5—Just as long as whatever you think is better
   isn't a competitive stainless steel razor blade.

1—Before he retired as a starting lineman with the
Green Bay Packers to take up a career in accounting.
2—Which consisted of beating the stuff with a stick
on a flat rock down by the creek behind our house.
3—Including the ones that were supposed to stay Navy Blue

1—The Hollywood Training School for Child Actors.
2—He'd receive an A+ in "Product-Testimonial Sincerity".
3—For the usual fee, of course.
4—Or any other normal toothpaste ingredients. In fact,
   I think it was airplane glue in unmarked tubes.
5—Which is what was expected, since I had 43% fewer teeth.

1—Because if I'd had to stand after seeing how long he talked, my feet would've given out.

2—But I was wrong about that. With the fat commission the Agent collects, I've also looked after his loved ones when he's gone.

3—Plus the help of all the money I could borrow to take out these new policies.

4—If my children ever get flexible enough to be educated.

5—Which would've been nice, except that I had to sell my home to buy the policies to protect the investment I don't have any more.

6—Now the only financial worries I'll have in my retirement years is where to get money to pay my insurance premiums.

THE
LIGHTER
SIDE OF
THE
BOSS

When I came to this town, I only had **$23** in my pocket! So I took a job for **$15 a week**—and worked **8 hours a day—5 days a week**—with **2 weeks vacation**!

But I was ambitious, so I **struggled** and **saved** and kept my nose to the **grindstone** until I finally went into business for **myself**!

Today, I'm the **Boss**! I'm a big **success**!

Now I work **18 hours a day**—**7 days a week**—with **no** vacations—and I **owe** my creditors over **$50,000**!

IN INJUN TERRITORY

DINK-DINK-DINK-DINK

PINK-DINK-DINK-DINK

DINK
DINK
DINK
DINK

Some time back (MAD #81), we published "The MAD Plan For Beating TV Commercial Breaks" which offered suggestions and methods for effectively, productively and enjoyably filling the valuable time taken up by idiotic TV ads. Now, MAD offers the following article for those lazy slobs who just cannot bring themselves to leave their TV set for something constructive ... who just sit there, enduring the pain of those ridiculous commercials. For you, MAD has created these

TV-COMMERCIAL AIDS

OR, HOW TO LIVE WITH TELEVISION COMMERCIALS— AND STILL NOT GO OUT OF YOUR EVER-LOVIN' MIND

ARTIST & WRITER: AL JAFFEE

Suddenly, the commercial comes on like a 21-gun salute—and the viewer must make a mad dash to the set in order to turn down the volume. Then he's got to stand there for three or four minutes while five or six commercials are run off and the program resumes. Only then can he dare to turn the volume up again and return wearily to his seat.

Aside from appealing to the moronic, the neurotic and the just-plain-sick, there's another irritating aspect to all TV commercials. This is especially apparent during late evening hours when the typical TV viewer is straining to catch the sound that has been purposely tuned very low so as not to disturb sleeping children or crabby neighbors.

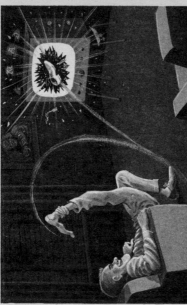

Some lucky set owners have remote control units that can turn sound down from across the room. But vast majority of viewers do not own them, and must run back and forth 20 or 30 times an hour to control commercial nuisance.

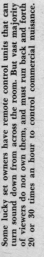

Many ingenious TV viewers, when they can no longer stand it, have spontaneously created a primitive form of remote control like the one shown above. Unfortunately, this has its limitations since it can only be used once an evening.

A SIMPLE REMOTE SOUND-CONTROL DEVICE THAT ANYONE CAN MAKE VIEWER ENJOYING HOMEMADE "TV-COMMERCIAL SOUND-OFF" DEVICE

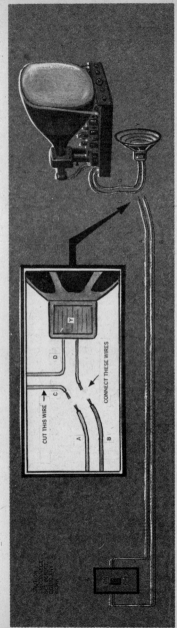

This is a simple Remote Control unit which any idiot can assemble and install, so ask an idiot to help you. Wires A and B lead from ordinary "On-Off" switch X (purchased at any hardware store) to TV set speaker Y. Note that TV speaker has two wires C and D which come from TV chassis. Cut one of these and connect ends of A and B to cut ends of speaker wire as shown in close-up drawing. Tape bare splices, and your Remote Control is ready for operation.

AND NOW A MESSAGE FROM CLICK!

Imagine! Now—with this simple Remote Control Unit—just a flick of your finger and you've knocked off the sound and rendered ineffective an offensive TV commercial! And what fun it is, when you realize that you're destroying a commercial that cost a sponsor maybe $50,000 or more to produce with a switch that cost you maybe 50¢ to produce!

ADDITIONAL COMPONENTS THAT COULD MAKE TELEVISION VIEWING ALMOST WORTHWHILE

For the really dedicated TV-Commercial hater, the simple Remote Control "Sound-Off" Unit may not be enough. So here are more sophisticated approaches to the problem. These can be assembled and instal-led in one or more units, depending upon how much time and money one wants to waste on this silly business. Just look how much of it has been spent already just to bring you this ridiculous article.

FUNNY MOUTHINGS UNIT

For many, a silent picture on TV may seem out of place, so this light-hearted device can be fun. It consists of pre-taped hilarious dialogue which replaces the words of the commercial announcer when his sound is knocked off, and makes his pitch even more idiotic than it actually is.

MUSICAL INTERLUDE UNIT

For those who may find ridiculous dialogue synchronized with a TV-commercial equally boring, this simple unit can be employed. It consists of recorded musical selections which start playing automatically when sound is knocked off. You listen to soothing melody while announcer mimes.

MOST COMPLETE REMOTE CONTROL UNIT POSSIBLE

Since a still picture is a poor substitute for live TV, this all-in-one unit will solve every problem. A motion picture projector unit is coupled with all the others to go on when sound is knocked off. Along with pre-selected travel pictures or action shots, the viewer can employ funny mouthings, or musical accompaniment or combination of both. In fact, when TV programs themselves are bad, it provides good uninterrupted feature-length entertainment.

DRAW CURTAIN UNIT

This component is designed for those viewers who prefer not to have their musical interludes marred by repugnant pictures. It automatically closes curtain over TV screen when music comes on, eliminating disgusting views of bad breath, gassy stomachs, etc., so viewer can eat a snack.

STILL PICTURE UNIT

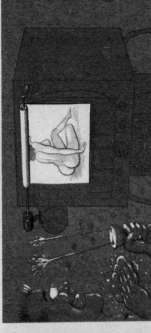

For those viewers who would not be satisfied to stare at a blank curtain while listening to a musical interlude, this component can be added. It automatically unrolls a full-color photo that is both pleasant and inspirational to look at while listening to music and eating a snack.

MOST EFFECTIVE REMOTE CONTROL UNIT POSSIBLE

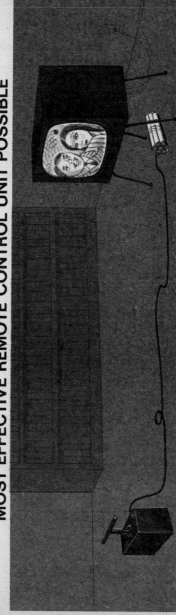

However, after carefully checking out this season's TV offerings, we've come to the conclusion that the programs are just as irritating as the commercials, and that this is the best remote control unit you can use. Now, instead of exposing yourself to television brain-rot, your mind can be elevated and nurtured by more worthwhile pursuits. Like reading, f'rinstance. And we're not talking about reading this rag, you clod! Try something constructive!

And now, in the tradition of "Flying Ace" (MAD #93)
and "Son Of Mighty Joe Kong" (MAD #94) which you
all loved . . . er—liked . . . well—*tolerated* . . . MAD once
again returns to the era of "Gutsy Movies" when men
were men, women were women, and would-be musicians
preferred to become Prize Fighters because they had

CRAZY FISTS

Illustrated by Mort Drucker

Written by Dick De Bartolo

Frankie, don't **talk** like that! You break a mother's **heart!** And you don't exactly do wonders for the **liver! You forget** about fighting and go upstairs and practice your **Ocarina!** Someday, you're gonna play in **Carnegie Hall!** Besides, it'll give us a chance to use that corny old **"transition scene"**—where we see a **little boy** playing an Ocarina badly, growing up into a **handsome young man,** still playing an Ocarina badly!

Ma! MA-A-A-A-A!! Somebody goofed! It's the wrong **"Transition Scene"!**

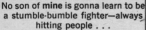

Well, kid—as the scene above shows, you've come a **long way!** And now you're ready for the **BIG ONE!**

I get to hit **Mona** for taking all the **good lines?**

Forget Mona! You're gonna fight the Champion— **"Detestable"** Dickens!

Great! I'll finish Dickens the **fastest yet!** I won't even **wait** for the "Weighing-In Ceremony"! Let's go over to his **house** right now! I'll show 'im . . . !

Politicians, celebrities, teachers, parents, businessmen . . . they're all making important statements these days. The trouble is, they usually say one thing, and mean another. And there's nobody around to translate for you ordinary clods! Except maybe us, the fearless men of MAD! (Who's around to translate the statements WE make that say one thing and mean something else is another problem!) Anyway, all this brings us to this next article, which offers examples to help you differentiate between—

WHAT THEY SAY ... AND WHAT IT REALLY MEANS

ARTIST: PAUL COKER JR.

WRITERS: RONALD AXE & SOL WEINSTEIN

WHEN THEY SAY...

...and starting next month, your Gas & Electric Company will be introducing **new, modern techniques** to serve you **faster** and **better!**

IT REALLY MEANS...

Another rate increase is on its way!

WHEN THEY SAY...

We have nothing **against** the boy, darling—it's just that you're **both** so terribly **young!**

IT REALLY MEANS...

Wait until you find a boy of your **own religion** who's got **money!**

WHEN THEY SAY...

The challenger is a **crafty, colorful, ring-wise veteran!**

IT REALLY MEANS...

He's a dirty fighter!

WHEN THEY SAY...

It's **not** the lousy **five dollars** you owe me—it's the **principle** of the thing!

IT REALLY MEANS...

It's the **lousy five dollars!**

WHEN THEY SAY...

IT REALLY MEANS...

WHEN THEY SAY...

It really means...

WHEN THEY SAY...

The **public** loved my book!

IT REALLY MEANS...

The critics **hated it!**

WHEN THEY SAY...

What an **unbelievable coincidence!** I had that **very same idea** recently!

IT REALLY MEANS...

Thanks for the idea!

NEW PRODUCT DIVISION

YOUR IDEAS WELCOME

WHEN THEY SAY...

IT REALLY MEANS...

WHEN THEY SAY...

I'd like to get **another professional opinion** in your case!

IT REALLY MEANS...

I'd like to **boost** your bill with some **"Fee-Splitting"**!

WHEN THEY SAY...

IT REALLY MEANS...

WHEN THEY SAY...

IT REALLY MEANS...

WHEN THEY SAY...

IT REALLY MEANS...

ON THE JOB

CHOMP!...
CHOMP CHOMP CHOMP

BLUE CHIPS OFF THE OLD BLOCK DEPT.

MAD, consumed with guilt, feels that it owes something to lovable ol' Charli Schulz, the creator of "Peanuts": Two of his very successful books: "*Happiness Is A Warm Puppy*" and "*I Can Use All The Friends I Can Get*" were the inspiration for two very successful MAD satires: "*Misery Is A Cold Hot Dog*" and "*I Got All The Finks I Need*". So now, by way of returning the favor, and since turnabout is fair play, we are publishing the following article in hopes that it will inspire Mr. Schulz to write another successful book.

BEING RICH IS BETTER THAN A WARM PUPPY

ARTIST & WRITER: AL JAFFEE

Being rich is having someone else put things back where you got them from.

Being rich is never being told to save your money for a rainy day.

Being rich is being able to buy
all the Bubble Gum you want
just to get the Trading Cards.

Being rich is getting clothes
you don't have to grow into.

Being rich is not having
to sneak food to your dog.

**Being rich is being able to afford to have
your neighborhood bully taken care of.**

Being rich is having all the wood you need to build things.

Being rich is not having to change your clothes before you can go out and play.

Being rich is having parents who buy all your Girl Scout Cookies.

**Being rich is not getting
scolded for losing things.**

Being rich is being allowed to play in any room of the house.

Being rich is being able to lend money to all your pals without worrying about getting it back.

Being rich is having your own room, even though you have brothers.

**Being rich is owning a ball
for every kind of game
so you won't be left out.**

**Being rich is not worrying
about over-due Library books.**

**Being rich is having someone to
take care of your kid sister.**

**Being rich is not getting one
single useful or practical gift
for Christmas or your birthday.**

**Being rich is getting a reward for
doing something that every other
kid has to do for nothing.**

**Being rich is having a Daddy who can
take you places, even during the day
in the middle of the week.**

Being rich is always getting sandwiches with the crusts cut away.

Being rich is getting brand new clothes when you need them, even though you have lots of older sisters.

Being rich is getting every Sunday Newspaper that has Color Comics.

Being rich is visiting your Father's office and not worrying how you behave.

**Being rich is knowing at least one grown-up
who doesn't treat you like a stupid kid.**

Being rich is being able to invite anyone you want to eat over.

Being rich is borrowing on next week's allowance and your parents never remembering it.

Being rich is breaking all your toys right after Christmas, and no one caring.

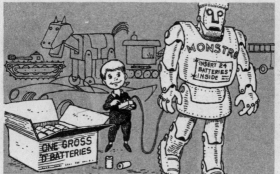

**Being rich is getting new batteries for all
your toys as soon as you need them.**

**Being rich is having all the pets you want
and not having to take care of them.**

**Being rich is having parents who worry if you got hurt
even when you accidentally break something expensive.**

**Being rich is leaving food on your plate and not getting
a lecture about how people are starving in Europe.**

A

FRIGHTFUL

INCIDENT

A MAD LOOK AT AT GARBAGEMEN

ARTIST & WRITER: SERGIO ARAGONES

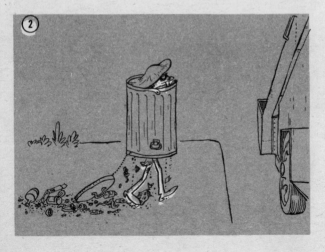

THE INDIGNANT HUSBAND

Recently, bleeding-heart liberal newspapers kicked up quite a fuss when it was learned that, in several cities throughout the United States, some members of the local Police Force are also members of the super-patriotic "John Birch Society". And so, in order to clear the air and assure everyone concerned that a Law Enforcement Officer, dedicated to "The Birch Society" can also do his job and protect members of "The Great Society"

MAD INTERVIEWS A

"JOHN BIRCH SOCIETY"

POLICEMAN

ARTIST: JOE ORLANDO   WRITERS: RONALD AXE & SOL WEINSTEIN

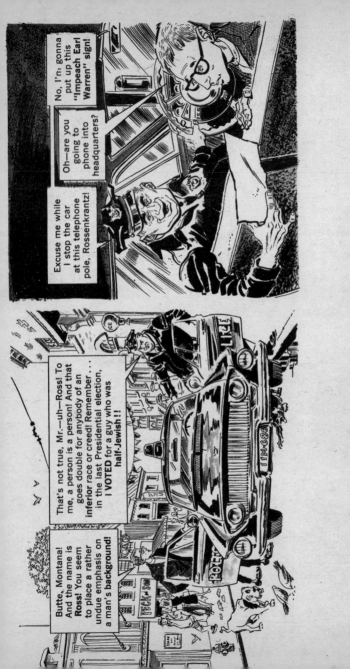

In our last issue, Dave Berg took a look at "The Lighter Side of The Boss"! However, after *our* Boss took a look at the article, Dave cooled him off with this follow-up...

THE LIGHTER SIDE OF EMPLOYEES

WRITER & ARTIST: DAVID BERG

Hello, **Alice**? This is **Amy**! What a **night** I had last night! I went out with **Bill**, and after dinner, he . . . Hold on . . .

Kaputnik Enterprises! I'll **connect** you!

Alice? So he says to me, "I want you to meet my **Mother** tonight" . . . Hold on . .

Kaputnik Enterprises! Good morning! Mr. Gumpky? Just a **moment**! I'll **connect** you!

Alice? So—thinking everything was on the up-and-up, I went to his **place**! But when we got there . . . Hold on . .

Kaputnik Enterprises! Good morning! Just **one moment**! I'll **connect** you!

Alice? Well, there was **no Mother** there! It was a **Bachelor Apartment** . . . Hold on!

Kaputnik Enterprises! Good morning! Mr. Zupp? Just a **moment**! I'll **connect** you!

Alice? So—the minute the door closed behind me, he starts looking at me like I was Gina Lolapalooza . . . Hold on . . .

Kaputnik Enterprises! I'll connect you!

So I says, "I'll have you know I'm **not** that kind of **girl!**" But that don't **stop** him! He **grabs me**, and . . . Hold on . . .

Kaputnik Enterprises! I'll connect you!

AMY! FOR PETE'S SAKE, SHUT DOWN THE SWITCHBOARD! I DON'T WANT ANY INCOMING CALLS FOR THE THE NEXT FIFTEEN MINUTES!!

Yes, Mr. Kaputnik!

Now, maybe we can **hear** how this **comes out** without any more **interruptions!**

Alice? So—anyway—he **grabs me** and . . .